D0229324

REMEMBER 10 WITH EXPLORER BEN

CATHERINE VEITCH   ILLUSTRATED BY **DUNCAN BEEDIE**

WITH MEMORY TECHNIQUES BY
TRACY PACKIAM ALLOWAY, PHD

© 2017 Quarto Publishing plc

First published in the UK in 2017 by QED Publishing
an imprint of The Quarto Group.
The Old Brewery, 6 Blundell Street,
London N7 9BH, United Kingdom.
T (0)20 7700 6700 F (0)20 7700 8066
www.QuartoKnows.com

A catalogue record for this book is available
from the British Library.

ISBN 978 1 91241 327 0

Publisher: Maxime Boucknooghe
Editorial Director: Laura Knowles
Art Director: Susi Martin
Designer: Verity Clark

Originated in Hong Kong by Bright Arts

Manufactured in Dongguan, China TL112017

9 8 7 6 5 4 3 2 1

CONTENTS

A Memory-boosting Adventure

This book combines a fun adventure story with a memory game, and along the way, it teaches children a variety of techniques to help them boost their memory.

Follow Explorer Ben on a journey around the world, stopping off at exciting places such as the desert and the Arctic. Each journey is split into two parts.

In the first part, Ben shows the reader the ten things he needs to pack, and the reader is introduced to a Memory Top Tip to help them remember those ten items.

In the second part, butter-fingered Ben has lost some of his things! He needs the reader's help to remember what's gone missing! As the book progresses, the challenges get harder, as Ben loses more of his belongings.

WHY DO I WANT TO HELP MY CHILD IMPROVE THEIR MEMORY SKILLS?

It has been shown that training your memory helps to improve focus and concentration. Creative memory techniques also enhance problem-solving abilities and creative thinking. Equipped with these skills, children become better learners. Improved memory techniques have also been shown to enhance children's social skills, as they increase children's confidence and their ability to remember instructions and make independent decisions.

EXPLORING THE BOOK WITH YOUR CHILD

While older children might like to explore the book independently, younger children may need support to master each memory technique and help Explorer Ben remember which items he's lost, so make it into a fun game. At the end of the book, parents will find notes on further ways they can help their child improve their memory and concentration.

Hello explorers! Grab your rucksacks and come on an adventure with me, Explorer Ben!

I'm off on a journey around the world, but there are so many things I must remember to pack.

Ben needs to take 10 things to the Amazon Rainforest. Can you help Ben remember everything he needs to pack? Use the MEMORY TOP TIP to help.

torch

binoculars

sleeping bag

insect spray

compass

penknife

Up, up and away!
First stop: the
Amazon rainforest.

water
bottle

tent

hat

book

EXPLORE
THE AMAZON

MEMORY TOP TIP
Make up a funny picture for
each thing, as funny pictures are
easier to remember. Here are
some silly pictures for Ben's
water bottle and his compass.

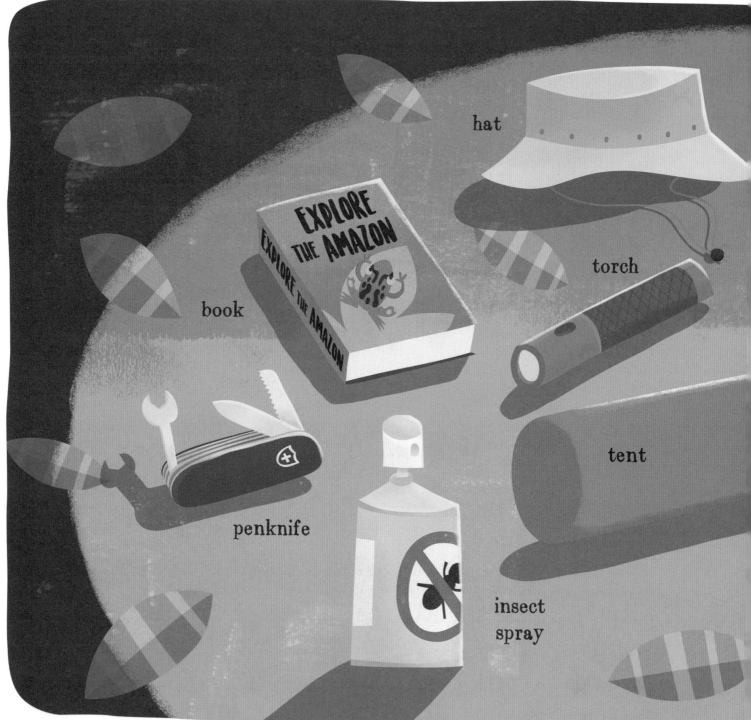

book

hat

torch

tent

penknife

insect
spray

water
bottle

compass

?

sleeping
bag

A cheeky monkey has
stolen ONE of my
things. Can you remember
what's missing?

Off to the Arctic now! Thanks for remembering my binoculars. They will be useful on this adventure too.

Remember 10 things to take on Ben's Arctic adventure.

coat

scarf

gloves

snowmobile

camping stove

Leap on to my snowmobile and come along for the ride. Whoa! Hold on tight!

boots

camera

book

THE ARCTIC

Veggie Soup

vegetable soup

goggles

MEMORY TOP TIP
Make up a little story that includes all ten things. Remember this story or make up one of your own.

Ben read a BOOK about the Arctic. Then he ordered a SNOWMOBILE, some GLOVES, GOGGLES and a SCARF. Next he cooked some VEGETABLE SOUP on his CAMPING STOVE for lunch. Then the doorbell rang. Ben looked out of the window and saw his shopping had arrived. He put on his COAT and BOOTS and rushed outside with his CAMERA to take a photo of his new, shiny snowmobile.

11

?

snowmobile

goggles

camping stove

Oh dear! I lost TWO things when I fell down the slippery slope! Can you remember what's missing?

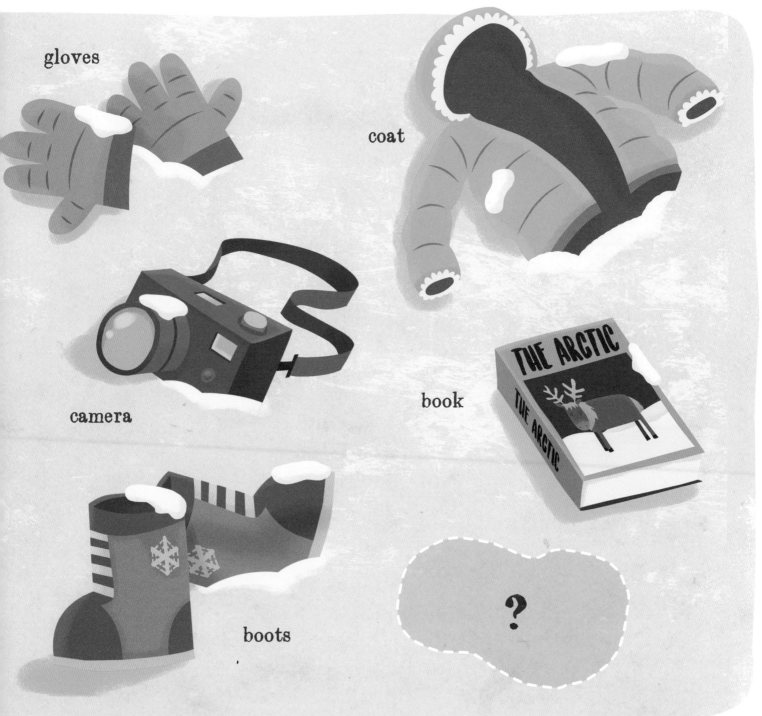

gloves

coat

camera

book

boots

?

I need to go somewhere warmer now. This camel will be great for exploring my next place, but I hope he behaves!

book

THE DESERT

THE DESERT

camel

sunglasses

spade

Remember 10 things to take on Ben's desert adventure.

sun hat

CEREAL BAR

cereal bar

sun cream

bucket

fan

headscarf

MEMORY TOP TIP
Make up a little rhyme
that includes all ten things.
Remember this rhyme or
make up one of your own.

50

Give me my BOOK,
And let's take a look
At the hump-backed CAMEL
— what a funny animal!
Grab my SUNGLASSES and my SUN HAT,
My SUN CREAM too — but just a pat.
Here's my BUCKET and my SPADE.
See the sandcastles I've made.
If I get hot, there's my HEADSCARF and FAN,
I'll bring a CEREAL BAR too,
that's a very good plan!

camel

headscarf

?

That naughty camel dumped me in the waterhole and I lost THREE things in the water. Can you remember what's missing?

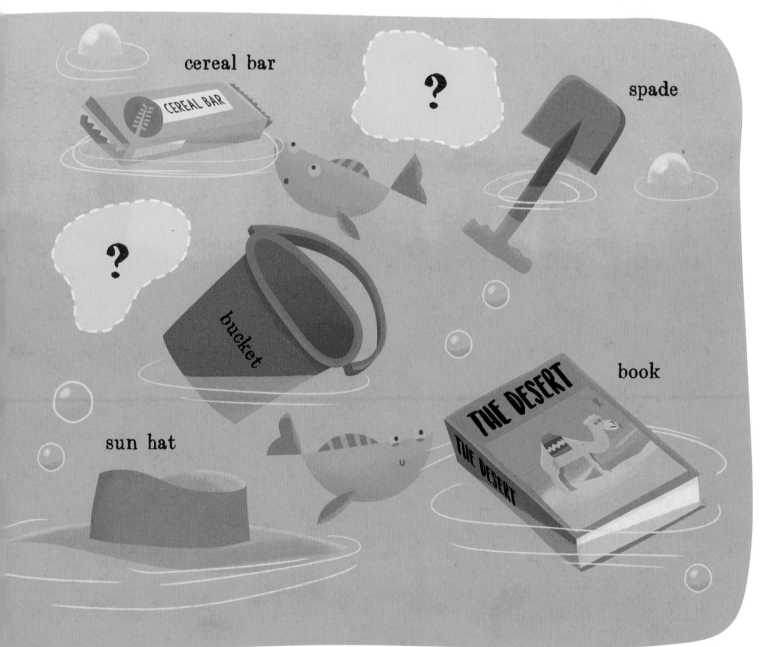

cereal bar

spade

book

bucket

sun hat

I'm super excited to go on Safari next, where I hope to film some amazing animals. Jump in my jeep and come along.

SAFARI

Remember 10 things to take on Ben's safari adventure.

First, Ben goes to his **BEDROOM**

...then he goes downstairs

STAIRS

onesie

blanket

satellite phone

...then he goes to the **BATHROOM**

...next he goes into his **STUDY**

ON SAFARI

MAP

first-aid kit

book

map

sandwich

...and into the
**CUPBOARD
UNDER THE
STAIRS**

...then he goes
into to the
KITCHEN
to make
a sandwich.

video
camera

rope

...Finally, Ben goes
into the **GARAGE**.

MEMORY TOP TIP
Close your eyes and
imagine Ben walking around
his house to pick up all ten
things. Imagine this journey
or a journey around
your own home.

jeep

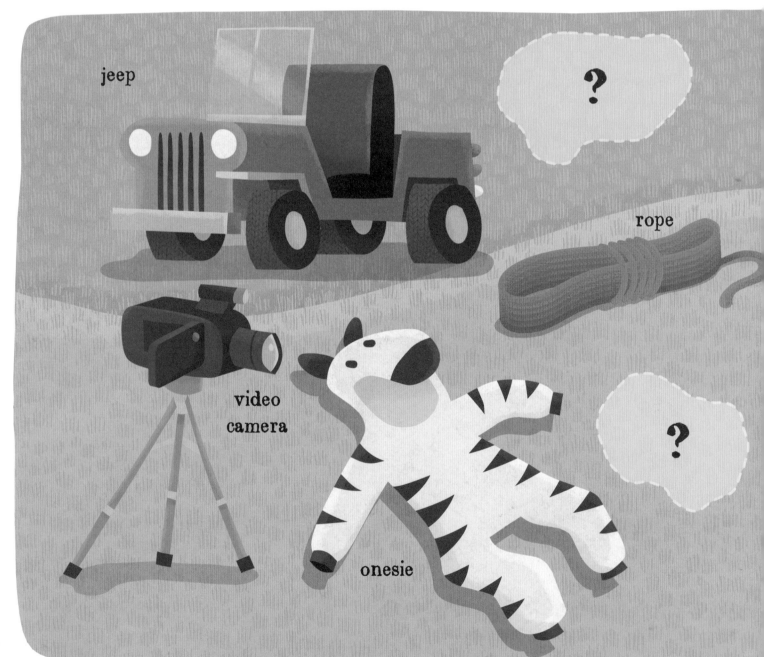

jeep

?

rope

video
camera

?

onesie

blanket

first-aid kit

Oh dear, I lost FOUR things while I was filming. Can you remember what's missing?

I'm off to climb a mountain next. Jump aboard this train and we'll be there in a flash!

Remember 10 things to take on Ben's mountain adventure.

book

MIGHTY MOUNTAINS

jacket

walking pole

bobble hat

列車チケット

ticket

kettle

skis

boots

ski poles

whistle

MEMORY TOP TIP
It's easier to remember things when they are in pairs. Remember these pairs, or make up some of your own.

SKIS	—	you also need SKI POLES
BOOTS	—	better with a WALKING POLE
TICKET	—	in the pocket of the JACKET
BOOK	—	fits inside the BOBBLE HAT
WHISTLE	—	KETTLE: both make a noise!

I lost FIVE things on my way down the mountain. Maybe it wasn't a good idea to ski down! Can you remember what's missing?

?

skis

?

ski poles

?

24

boots

jacket

walking pole

Ahoy me hearties! Are you ready to go snorkelling with me? Right then, let's set sail.

Remember 10 things to take on Ben's snorkelling adventure.

flag

cheese

rubber ring

MEMORY TOP TIP
Make up a picture in your mind of each thing on Ben.

Imagine Ben in his WETSUIT, wearing his FLIPPERS, SNORKEL, FACE MASK, LIFE JACKET and a RUBBER RING. He carries a FLAG, and has a CAMERA around his neck, while reading his BOOK and eating CHEESE!

face mask

snorkel

book

camera

wetsuit

life jacket

flippers

CORAL REEF

snorkel

Some mischievous pelicans stole SIX of my things. Can you remember what's missing?

?

flippers

wetsuit

flag

plate

mug

FRESH!

toothpaste

THE OUTBACK
THE OUTBACK

book

MEMORY TOP TIP
Act out using each of Ben's ten things. For example, copy these actions, or make up some of your own.

- Play an imaginary GUITAR.

- Open an imaginary FLASK, pour out the drink into a MUG and lift it to your mouth.

- Fry some imaginary SAUSAGES in an imaginary FRYING PAN.

- Pick up the sausages with an imaginary SPOON and put them on a PLATE.

- Put some imaginary TOOTHPASTE on a TOOTHBRUSH and pretend to brush your teeth.

- Read an imaginary BOOK.

book

spoon

frying pan

Those pesky animals stole SEVEN of my things. Can you remember what's missing?

It's good to get away from that hot weather. It will be cooler exploring this cave.

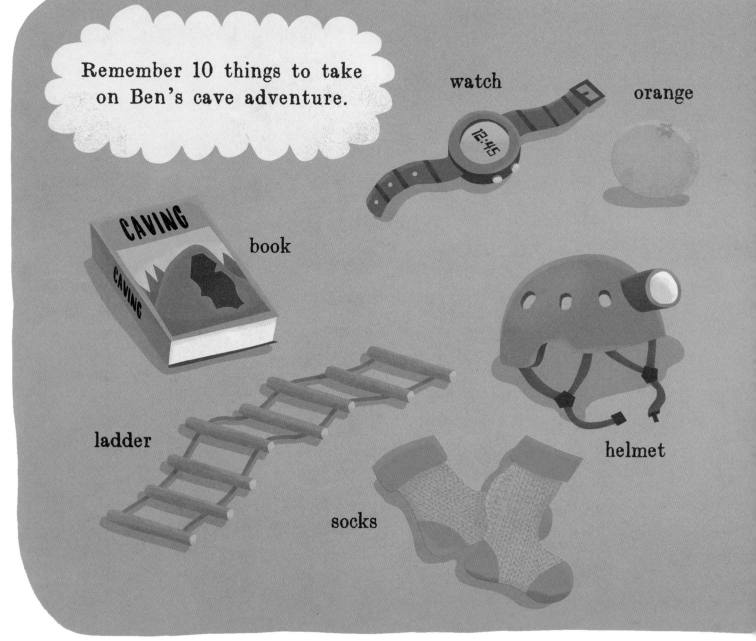

Remember 10 things to take on Ben's cave adventure.

watch

orange

book

CAVING

ladder

socks

helmet

spade

gloves

MEMORY TOP TIP
Match each of Ben's ten things to a colour of the rainbow. For example, remember these or make up some of your own.

cable

wellies

red CABLE

orange SOCKS and orange ORANGE

yellow WELLIES and yellow GLOVES

green LADDER and green SPADE

blue HELMET

indigo BOOK

violet WATCH

gloves

socks

It was so dark and
cramped in that cave
that I lost EIGHT things.
Can you remember
what's missing?

Thanks for helping me find my things. Join me for some white water rafting next, if you dare!

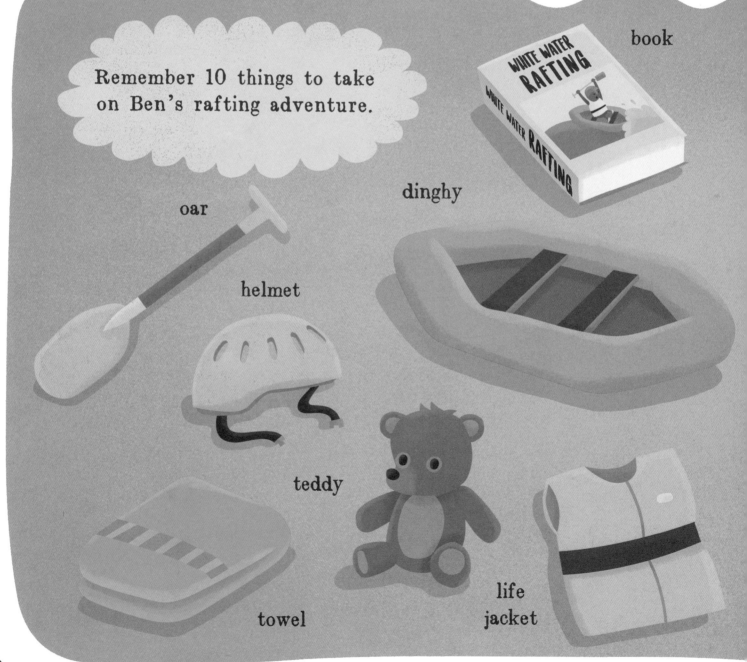

Remember 10 things to take on Ben's rafting adventure.

book

oar

dinghy

helmet

teddy

towel

life jacket

MEMORY TOP TIP
Describe each of Ben's ten things with a word that begins with the same first letter. For example, remember these descriptions or make up some of your own.

rubber duck

trainers

umbrella

big BOOK ✓
dinky DINGHY ✓
lovely LIFE JACKET ✓
ugly UMBRELLA ✓
tall TEDDY ✓
old OAR ✓
hard HELMET ✓
tiny TOWEL ✓
tight TRAINERS ✓
round RUBBER DUCK

dinghy

I can't wait to fly as high as the clouds in my hot air balloon. Come up, up, up and away with me!

Remember 10 things to take on Ben's balloon adventure.

book

bunting

teaspoon

chair

table

teapot

cup

tea

milk

MEMORY TOP TIP
Make up a song that
includes all of Ben's ten things.
Remember this song to the tune of
'Twinkle, Twinkle, Little Star', or
make up one of your own.

Flying high up in the air
with my TABLE and my CHAIR.

Bright BUNTING and a pretty view,
a TEAPOT, CUP and SAUCER too.

Stir the MILK with my TEASPOON,
drinking TEA all afternoon.

I'll read my BOOK and look around,
there's lots to see above the ground.

saucer

Oh dear, I lost all
TEN of my things!
I'll check the weather
before I go hot air
ballooning next time.
Can you remember
what's missing?

THE MOON

Marvellous Memory Quiz

Do you have a marvellous memory? Have a go at this quiz to find out.

1. Ben made up funny pictures to remember his things in the Amazon Rainforest. What was the picture he made up for his water bottle?

   A)   B)   C)

2. What snowy creature made Ben jump in the Arctic?

   A)   B)   C)

3. Ben made up a rhyme with the things he took to the desert. Which word would you choose to help you remember your coat?

   A) Rabbit   B) Goat   C) Bear

4. Which two animals did Ben spot on safari?

   A)   B)   C)

5. It helped Ben to remember his things in pairs. Can you remember what he paired with his ski poles for the mountain?

    A) Bucket   B) Kettle   C) Skis

6. Which two sea creatures did Ben meet on his snorkelling trip?

    A)   B)   C)

7. Ben acted out using the things he took to Australia.
    Do some actions that will help you to remember these things.

    A) Jelly   B) Bathtub   C) Clock

8. Ben matched each thing he took caving to a colour.
    Can you remember which colour Ben matched his socks with?

    A) Yellow   B) Blue   C) Orange

9. Ben matched each thing he took rafting to a word with the
    same first letter. Which word would you choose to help you
    remember your toothbrush?

    A) Long   B) Tickly   C) Smelly

10. Ben's hot air balloon was in the shape of an animal.
    Can you remember what it was?

    A) Cat

    B) Bear

    C) Fish

Don't worry if you couldn't answer all the questions. The more you practise, the better your memory will be!

Answers: 1=B; 2=A; 3=B; 4=B and C; 5=C; 6=A and B; 8=C; 9=B; 10=B.

47

TOP TIPS FOR PARENTS

Here are five more steps you can take to help improve your child's memory skills (and your own!). All of these are scientifically proven to benefit memory and concentration.

1. SLEEP ON IT

Learning just before bedtime is a great way to boost memory of that information. Studies show that a good night's sleep after learning helps the brain consolidate and remember new information better compared to when you learn it in the morning.

2. GO BLUE

A healthy diet is crucial for optimal brain function, but some foods have been shown to be especially good for your memory. Blueberries don't just taste great – they're also a bit of a wonder fruit when it comes to boosting memory. Multiple studies have found that the flavonoids in this fruit are the reason behind cognitive benefits at all ages.

3. CLIMB A TREE

Scientific research has shown the cognitive benefits of being 'proprioceptively dynamic'. That sounds fancy, but it means doing physical activities such as crawling, balancing and climbing trees. Just two hours of this sort of physical activity can improve working memory by 50 percent... and it's good for your body too!

4. DOODLE

Doodling while you work on a boring task can actually improve attention and working memory, according to one study. When you doodle, you are less likely to daydream or lose interest in the task.

5. DARK CHOCOLATE

This last tip might surprise you. Give your child dark chocolate to satisfy their sweet tooth. Studies show that people who ate dark chocolate (70% cocoa solids or higher) were more accurate in working memory tests and also responded faster compared to those who ate white chocolate. Just don't eat too much!

48